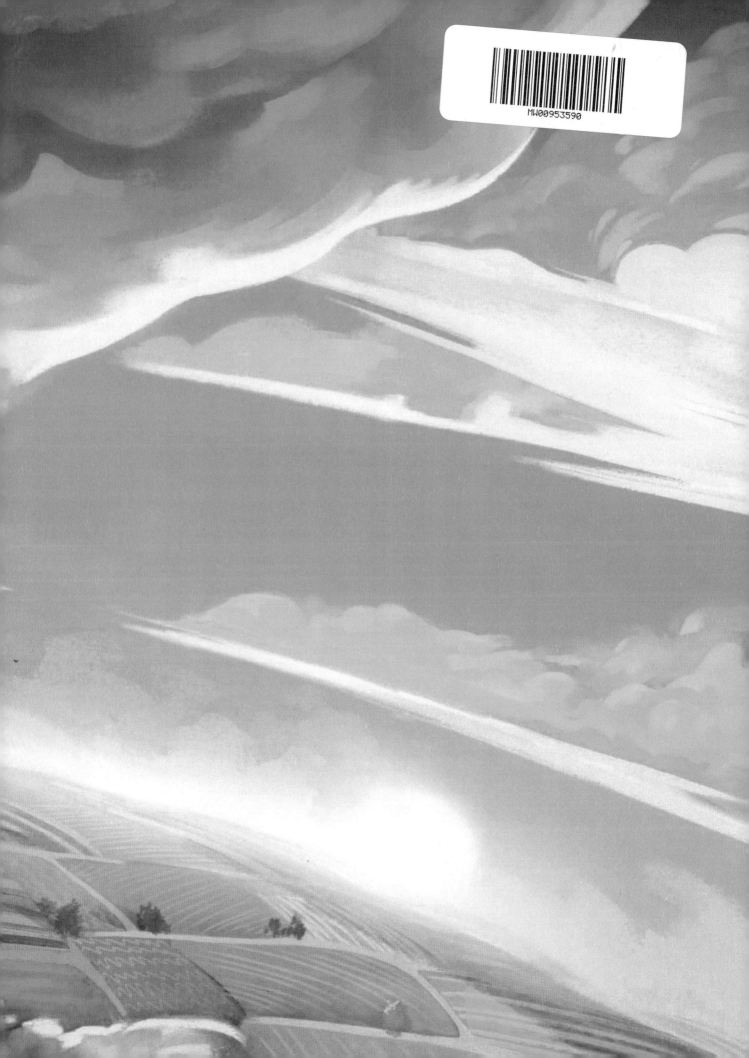

MW00953590

TO MY KIDS.
I SEE THE GIANT IN EACH OF YOU.

THIS BOOK BELONGS TO THE FOLLOWING GIANT:

THE GIANTS
AND THE
SMALLS™

THE ADVENTURE OF RIMI AND RITT

NICHOLAS TOWNSEND SMITH
ILLUSTRATED BY J. TUMBURUS

Beyond the night sky and further than the faintest star, past the darkest part of the heavens, is a world so big it would make our Earth look like a single grain of sand. The inhabitants of this great sphere lived strange lives that were, to a certain degree, like ours, but the most curious thing about them was that some were Giants, and many were Smalls.

The Giants and Smalls lived amongst each other and shared the world as so many of us do. They breathed the same air, had similar opportunities, and in many ways, were alike. However, they were massively different in size.

The Smalls kept to themselves, eating tiny crackers and pea soup and having Small talk. They believed that Smalls were small, and a Small is born a Small, lives a Small and dies a Small. They had strong beliefs about themselves. They never had thoughts of their little neighbors, even in insignificant ways. Smalls were afraid to do brave things because their minds were small, and they had always been small, so they went about in a small world, never having the courage to think big thoughts or take big risks. Their tiny feet led them down the same little paths, never brave enough to discover big things that would make them more exceptional in the heart.

McBronze Rittinshanks was born into a Small family and lived a small, ordinary life. His Small friends had a hard time saying such a large name, so he became known as Ritt. Ritt came from a family with a long history of being small, and as Ritt got older, he lived an insignificant life, traveled the same meager path his parents had taken, and associated with other Smalls, who lived, thought, and acted small.

Like most Smalls, Ritt only saw the path he was on and rarely looked up to see what else might be happening around him. One day, a burst of distant laughter high above him had him look to the sky. The Giants had always been nearby, but he never paid attention to them, and for some reason, that day, the sight of them sparked some fascinating questions.

"Why are there Giants?" he wondered.

"Why are they living such giant lives while I live this small one? How did they become so massive? Is it possible for me to become a giant?"

These were the first giant questions Ritt had ever asked. He had once heard that everyone could become a giant, but his parents' words rang in his mind, *"Giants are Giants and Smalls are Smalls, and that's the way it will always be!"*

Ritt shared his questions with some of his Small friends, who laughed at him. Smalls were good at belittling, after all. They told him, "It's not possible to become a Giant. You have to come from a certain ancestry or have extra special talents to be a Giant. Giants are unique!" they said. "You're just a regular ole Small!"

Ritt slumped to the curb with his head in his hands. "Maybe it's easier to be a Small than to stand out." But inside he knew he was more than a Small.

Time passed, and while traveling down the same small path he had always taken, Ritt saw the giants and asked himself, *"Is this all there is to life, staying small and afraid, not standing out or being different? Who would want to be small forever?"* he wondered. "Not me!" he exclaimed. "I want to do more!"

Ritt pondered how he could learn about the Giants. He couldn't ask his friends and family for they were all Smalls, and what do Smalls know about being Giants?!

"I've got it!" he said out loud. "Who would know more about being a Giant than a Giant?! I know just what I'll do."

The very next day, Ritt packed some small things into a tiny bag, he grabbed several pairs of his favorite striped socks and his hat—of course, gathered some crackers and a hunk of cheese for his adventure, left the path he had always taken, and journeyed to find a Giant.

As Ritt traveled, he made up a song, and as he walked he sang and whistled the tune,

"I would like to be like you and you could be with me, and we will go on to the moon to see what we can see. When my life gets too hard to do will you come set me free, and as you find a way to break through will you turn 'round and rescue me, because the way is not found alone and the only way 'can be won is by getting to somewhere that you've never known and do something you've never done . . . "

The path wasn't easy for Ritt, there were rivers to cross—Ritt loved playing in streams, so this wasn't terrible for him. He had forests to trek and long open spaces to cross where the sun beat down on him continuously. The heat at times was unbearable, but after a long journey—every journey being long for a Small—Ritt arrived at the place where the Giants lived.

They seemed so magnificent. He sat quietly for a moment and watched. Small, fearful thoughts began to fill his head.

"Will they step on me? Are they going to eat me?" he wondered.

"Who am I to ask a Giant these questions?"

Mustering up a small amount of courage and trusting that he was making the right choice, Ritt shook off these fearful thoughts and moved on.

Ritt approached a Giant. His whole body shivered as he looked up. The Giant's head was well above the clouds. His clothes were larger than life; similar to Ritt's, but substantially bigger. The Giant's Brown vest and white shirt were all that was visible through the clouds. A giant green hankie hung from the Giant's back pocket. It looked like an enormous flag blowing in the wind.

Ritt approached the massive being and began to climb. He hung on and climbed and climbed, and climbed. As he reached the Giant's shoulder, Ritt could no longer see the ground below. His head spun. His knees wobbled. He held on to the Giant's shirt collar to keep from falling. He had never been so far above the ground and was hanging on for dear life.

Gathering as much courage as he could, Ritt climbed up to the Giant's ear and yelled, "Mr. Giant!"

There was no answer.

Ritt tried again, "Mr. Giant!"

The Giant looked around and said, "Who was that? Who said that?"

Ritt yelled in his ear again, "Mr. Giant!"

The Giant roared again, "Who is that?"

Ritt covered his tiny ears. The Giant's voice shook his entire body. He could hardly understand what the Giant was saying because the sound was so immense.

"Mr. Giant," yelled Ritt, "I am a Small."

The Giant said, "A Small, here?" his voice vibrating and shaking Ritt. "What are you doing here?"

"I came to ask you how you became a Giant."

The Giant, moved by the courage of this tiny being, invited Ritt onto his hand. "What a brave thing to do." said the Giant.

Ritt sat against a fold in the Giant's hand and looked up into his enormous eyes. The Giant cleared his throat—a little choked-up by Ritt's bravery—and began to speak in a quieter tone.

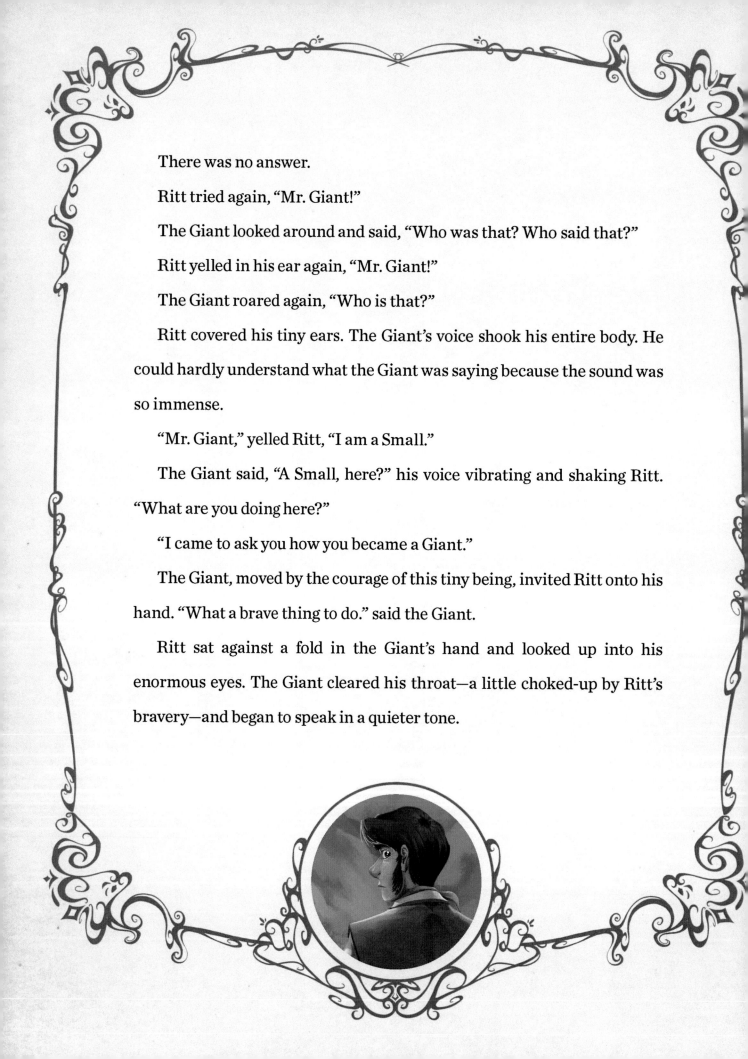

"I am impressed by your bravery. I haven't seen a Small in a very long time. I would be honored to share my story with you."

Ritt leaned forward as the Giant continued, "My parents were Giants, and they knew the path to become a Giant. They loved to explore the possibilities in the world around them; they dreamed impossible dreams, and always thought of others and how they could best serve them. My parents' hearts were enormous. They were constantly looking for ways to improve themselves, serve others, and make their world a better place. Their Giant feet took them down paths of endless possibility, and that helped them to reach their stature." Ritt gasped and leaned in even closer.

"My friend, I need you to know that I was born a Small just like you. At first," said the Giant, "I didn't think I could measure up to my parents' stature even though they taught me their ways from childhood. It took me years before I finally believed. When I finally started doing what they had told me all along, you know what happened?"

Ritt looked the Giant straight in the eyes and asked, "What?"

"Well, I began to grow."

"What do you mean?" asked Ritt.

The Giant said, "You see, Giants think extraordinary thoughts, speak significant words, and see and do remarkable things. As I began to learn, my hearing improved, and my vision expanded. That's what is magical about this world; by listening to my parents and doing what they did, I started to grow."

Ritt's thoughts were racing. Could this be true? This was madness. A Small became a Giant merely by thinking differently, and making new choices? That's the difference between the Giants and the Smalls? Did that mean he could become a Giant?

"There's only one way to find out," Ritt thought to himself. "Will you teach me how to become a Giant?" Ritt asked.

"Wow!" said the Giant. "This is a big thing you are asking me, and I don't know if you're up for the changes that will come if you go down this path. You're asking me to help you grow in a way you don't fully understand. How can I know that you will do what it takes to grow?"

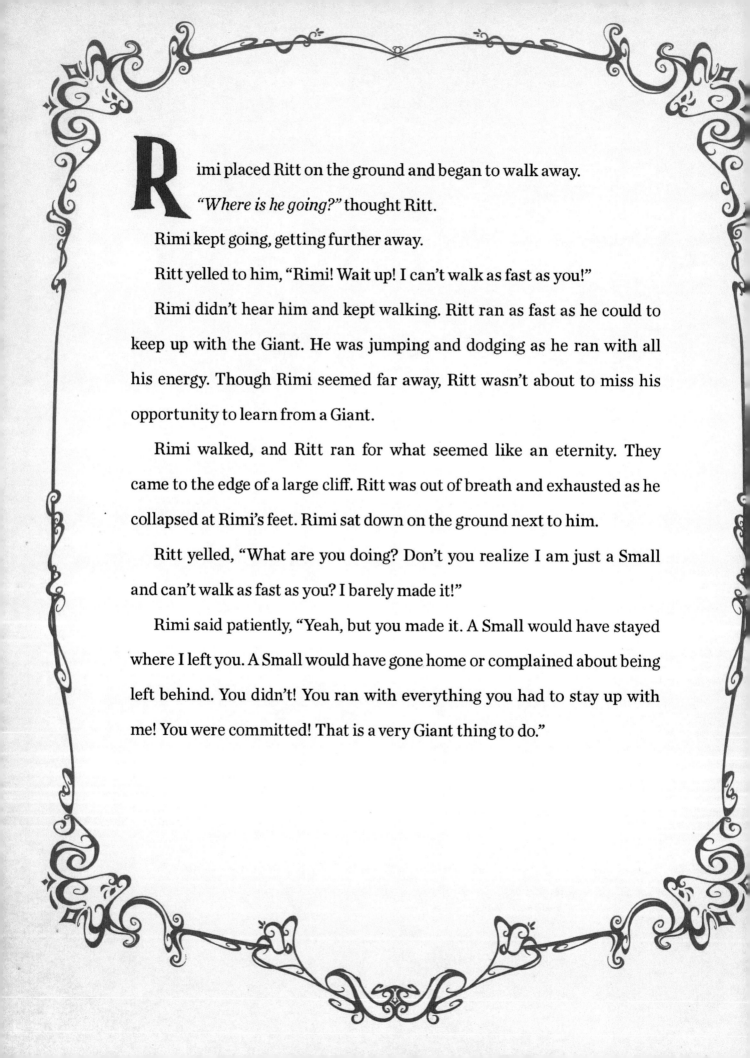

Rimi placed Ritt on the ground and began to walk away.

"Where is he going?" thought Ritt.

Rimi kept going, getting further away.

Ritt yelled to him, "Rimi! Wait up! I can't walk as fast as you!"

Rimi didn't hear him and kept walking. Ritt ran as fast as he could to keep up with the Giant. He was jumping and dodging as he ran with all his energy. Though Rimi seemed far away, Ritt wasn't about to miss his opportunity to learn from a Giant.

Rimi walked, and Ritt ran for what seemed like an eternity. They came to the edge of a large cliff. Ritt was out of breath and exhausted as he collapsed at Rimi's feet. Rimi sat down on the ground next to him.

Ritt yelled, "What are you doing? Don't you realize I am just a Small and can't walk as fast as you? I barely made it!"

Rimi said patiently, "Yeah, but you made it. A Small would have stayed where I left you. A Small would have gone home or complained about being left behind. You didn't! You ran with everything you had to stay up with me! You were committed! That is a very Giant thing to do."

As Ritt caught his breath, they both looked out at the cliff. Rimi seemed to be enjoying the view and asked his new friend, "What do you see?"

Ritt said, "I see a cliff, some plants, and the sky."

Rimi asked him, "What else do you see?"

"Nothing!" exclaimed Ritt.

Rimi laughed and placed Ritt on his shoulder. He stood up. A vast ocean spread out in front of them as far as the eye could see. Ritt could smell the ocean air and feel the breeze. It was the first time in his life he had seen such an amazing view.

Rimi asked him, "Now what do you see?"

Ritt couldn't speak. The view was so breathtaking that all he could do was look.

Rimi said, "Ritt, a Giant sees what a Small might never see. A Giant sees the beauty in everything, while a Small misses out on seeing the splendor that surrounds them. A Giant sees opportunity in every moment, and a Small only focuses on his or her problems."

Ritt looked up at Rimi and said, "I want to see what a Giant sees and do what a Giant does."

The sun was going down. Rimi told Ritt, "Go home and think about the lessons you've learned. Come back tomorrow." He carried Ritt back to where they had met, and Ritt headed home. That night as Ritt slept in his small bed, he had giant dreams for the first time.

The next morning, as he sat up in his bed, he banged his head on the ceiling. He fell backward, and his arm broke through the window. His small bed smashed to pieces beneath him.

"What's going on?" he howled.

During the night, he had grown. By thinking giant thoughts and dreaming giant dreams, he had actually grown. He stood up from his broken bed and hit his head on the ceiling again. He ran to the front door and squeezed out, breaking it to smithereens.

Ritt ran as fast as he could to the land of the Giants, stopping every Giant he saw to ask for his new friend, Rimi. He approached Rimi's home and pounded on the door frantically. "Rimi!" he yelled, "Rimi! Open up! It's me, Ritt!"

Rimi opened the door casually and looked at his friend. "Wow!" he laughed, "You've grown!"

"I know I've grown," said Ritt. "My house is destroyed, and I don't fit in it anymore. I don't know what to do."

R itt walked into the biggest home he had ever seen. It was a home built for a Giant. Rimi invited him to sit at the table. Ritt had never seen so much food. He was used to small pea soup and crackers, and here in front of him was more food than a Small could imagine: fruits and pastries, fresh meats, and the most excellent vegetables. Rimi instructed him to eat all that he wanted. There was more than enough.

Ritt ate and ate and ate. He ate the fruits. He ate the vegetables. He ate the meats and pastries, and as he did, he grew a little bit more.

He asked, "Why am I growing?"

Rimi said, "Ritt, a Giant sees the abundance of the world. He is grateful for things that a Small doesn't even see. A Giant knows there is more than enough of everything for everyone, and a Small does not. There's enough to share, and if something runs out, I can produce more."

Ritt thought about what Rimi said and finished his meal, his belly bulging, and his belt buckle loosened. He had never thought about abundance. Smalls were always saying there wasn't enough of anything. He never considered the idea that if one thing ran out, he could make more. He was beginning to see the plenty that surrounded him.

"The life you knew will never be the same," said Rimi, "and this is just the first step in becoming what you say you want to become. It's up to you whether you want to keep growing. What would you like to do?"

Ritt closed his eyes, shrugged his shoulders, and sighed. Shaking his head back and forth, he looked up at Rimi and said, "Well, I don't want to go back, and I definitely don't want to stay like this. I'm neither a Giant nor a Small; I want to keep going!"

Satisfied, Rimi smiled and invited his little friend inside. "Let's eat some breakfast, and we'll get to our next lesson."

He stood up from the table and walked to the window. "Rimi," he asked, "how is it that you have so much while the Smalls have so little?"

"Follow me!" Rimi said. He walked steadily outside to a large garden. Ritt followed. He had never seen such enormous plants and fruit trees. There were rows and rows of fruits and vegetables, and a small farm filled with animals.

Ritt asked Rimi, "What are you doing?"

Rimi said, "We! We are working in the garden. This is where the food you were eating came from. A Giant works to earn the things he or she has, and you, my friend, will be working with me today. We will be pulling weeds and taking care of the plants, the fruit trees, and the animals."

Suddenly Ritt noticed not only the plants but the weeds. They were gigantic. *"How in the world could a Small pull such big weeds and take care of such a large garden?"* he thought.

Rimi handed Ritt some gloves and started working; Ritt did too. He tugged and tugged on those weeds. At first, they wouldn't budge. His hands hurt and were swollen and blistered. A giant beetle jumped out, and Ritt fell over backward, trying to get out of the way. He started laughing as he realized it had no interest in him.

Ritt had never worked so hard in his entire small life. The task felt impossible, but the more he worked, the stronger he got, the easier it became, and the bigger he grew. They spent the whole day working.

Ritt was covered in dirt and sweat and smelled worse than the animals.

"You did well," Rimi said. "It was hard for you at first, but the more you did, the better you got. A Giant knows that when he starts something new, he won't be very good at it. If he's willing to keep doing it, his skills will improve until one day he can do it without thinking."

"Rimi, can I ask you something?"

Rimi said, "Yes."

Ritt said, "Can you..."

"Yes," Rimi said before Ritt could finish.

Ritt looked at him, confused, "How can you say 'yes' if you don't even know what I am going to ask?"

Rimi said, "There's nothing you can ask that's bigger than me. I can do anything you ask. The question is, will I?"

Ritt thought about that. *"There is nothing this Giant can't do? That sounds impossible; how can he do everything?"* He was so stunned by Rimi's answer he had forgotten what it was he was going to ask.

Ritt was still thinking about what Rimi had said when Rimi spoke. "Ritt, you have that same gift. In fact, all Smalls and Giants can do anything. Smalls tell themselves all the reasons why they can't do something, and that keeps them from becoming Giants."

Rimi and Ritt continued working the garden into the woods. In their deep conversations and hard work, they lost track of time. The sun went down, and it was time to head home.

As they walked through the forest, Ritt couldn't see his hand in front of his face. He cautiously felt his way through the trees and vines. Ritt's pants snagged on a thorn, and he fell behind. He heard a flutter. His heart started pounding, and his stomach got tingly. A twig cracked nearby, and the hair on the back of his neck stood up. He imagined all of the frightening things that could be around him.

Suddenly, something brushed across his face. He screeched, swinging his hands wildly in front of him to get it away. He broke away from the thorn and started running wildly through the trees. He wondered what kind of creature was trying to get him, never realizing that his frightening encounter was just a leaf hanging from a branch.

Ritt could hear Rimi walking in front of him, but couldn't see him. He followed as quickly as he could. It felt like he was walking forever in the darkness, but he kept moving. He didn't want to be left behind. As he caught up to Rimi, tattered from the woods, Ritt said, short of breath, "You didn't seem afraid as you walked through that. You just kept going."

Rimi turned. "Ritt, I do get afraid occasionally, but a Giant keeps moving and doesn't allow fear to keep him from doing what he can do. Giants know that allowing fear to overtake them can make them smaller—this was a new thought for Ritt, he knew he could grow, but hadn't considered the idea that fearful thoughts could make him shrink. Smalls allow their imaginations to create scary stories about all the bad things that could happen. Giants put positive things in their minds and move forward despite their fears. A Giant knows that all fears are stories that we've made up. We can make the stories as scary or as beautiful as we would like. If I am in a place that I don't know, or that might be scary, I make up a positive story in my mind, and things turn out just fine."

That was a relief to Ritt. He liked the idea of making up new stories and certainly didn't want to shrink. Making new narratives sounded fun, so, instead of imagining all of the scary things in the darkness, he simply made up a new story. In place of terrifying creatures and monsters, he pictured happy little animals playing hide and seek in the dark. He imagined them laughing and telling stories with thoughts of him joining them in the silliness, and as he visualized this, he grew.

Ritt worked in every moment to do his best in everything he did. He worked every day at becoming a Giant. In time he built an enormous home, planted himself a prodigious garden, and began sharing his adventure with other Smalls—as many of the Smalls wondered what happened to Ritt after they discovered his house in shambles. Many of the Smalls learned from Ritt, and also became Giants.

Ritt had a lot of adventures with his friend Rimi and learned the ways of the Giants. It wasn't easy, and it took a lot of energy and effort for him to choose each day, whether he was going to be a Small or a Giant. Whether he would do giant things, ask giant questions, make giant decisions, or continue playing life as a Small. In the end, Ritt grew, and grew, and grew, and became a giant among Giants.

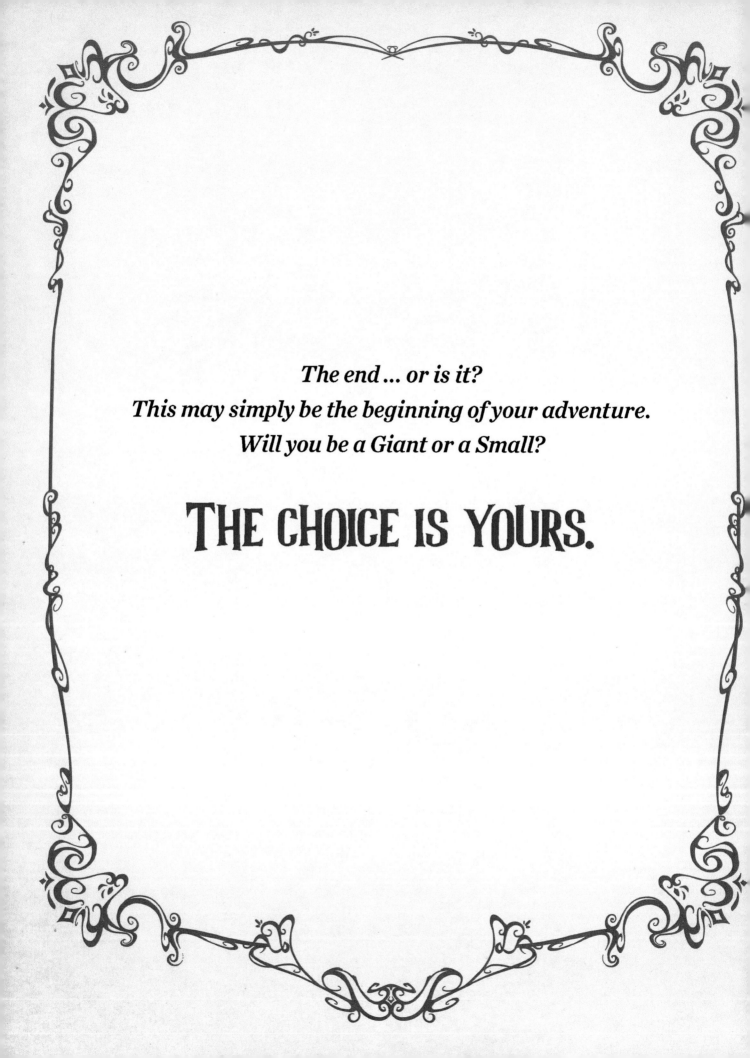

The end ... or is it?
This may simply be the beginning of your adventure.
Will you be a Giant or a Small?

THE CHOICE IS YOURS.

THE ORIGINS

I was feeling defeated. I was sitting in the parking lot of a food bank. My home was in foreclosure, I filed for bankruptcy, my wife lost respect for me, money was gone, and I felt smaller than I had at any other point in my life.

My identity at that time was wrapped up in the idea that my manliness, my worth, my whole purpose of being, was tied to my ability to provide. After the market crash of 2008, and some poor financial choices, that was all stripped away and all that was left was the chaos I invited in.

A friend of mine at the time, Julie Blake, said I needed to meet someone. She built this man up like he could help me shift my world.

I had a taste of coaching through a good friend of mine and was intrigued with the idea of coaching, writing, and speaking; I mean, who better to coach than someone who is in the pits of despair, right?! I agreed to talk with this person, Steve Hardison, and she arranged a call.

I didn't know when Steve would call; I just knew to watch for him. His call came through when I was at my lowest of lows. I was ready to walk into the food bank, and when I saw his number on my caller ID, I paused. I remember sitting in the front of our SUV (an older, tan Ford Expedition) and giving my full attention to this stranger.

I remember parts of the conversation, but that's not what stood out the most. What I remember most is how I felt. I mean, let's imagine you got a call from Jesus. How would that go?! I'm not implying this man is Jesus, but the love I felt in that conversation was as close to what I imagine a conversation with Jesus might be to anything I had experienced to that point in my life.

I felt like I was the only person in the world. Like it was him and I and that no one else existed. We were the only two people on the planet. We talked for nearly an hour, and that single conversation was pivotal in my life.

I remember asking Steve a question, something along the lines of, "Can you…," but before I could finish, he said, "Yes!" I didn't remember what I was going to ask because his answer was so sudden and unexpected that the only thing I could say was, "How can you say yes if you don't know what I am going to ask?" He answered, and I don't take this as a light answer, "There is nothing you can ask me that is beyond my ability to complete. There is nothing bigger than me. I can do anything!"

I didn't hear that from that space of arrogance or from a space of delusion; this man truly knew he could accomplish anything, whether by himself or with the support of others, he could achieve anything, and the answer stuck with me--like glue on my consciousness. It was so impactful that it became an integral part of what transpired.

After that conversation, my life didn't change drastically. I was still working with my brother in Park City, driving an hour in each direction, listening to audiobook after audiobook. At that time, if audiobooks came in IV form, I would have signed up.

I remember listening to "Who Moved My Cheese" by Spencer Johnson on one of those commutes. I remember thinking, "I could write this!" and so I did. I was inspired at that moment, but I didn't know what I would write. During my commute, I remember seeing the vast mansions up on the hill, and I wondered, "How did they get there? Why are they living such giant lives while I am living this small one? Is that possible for me?" The very questions you see in my book, The Giants and the Smalls: The Adventure of Rimi and Ritt.

I spoke that book into existence as I would drive to work. With a voice recorder in hand, Spencer Johnson's story fresh in my mind, the words of Steve Hardison bouncing around in my head, turning the reality I thought I knew into mush, like a chrysalis of creation, I recorded that book as I would commute. I would come home, transcribe it, share it with my kids, and adjust. It took nearly a year to get the foundation of the book.

I wrote this book standing on the shoulders of Giants, standing on the shoulder of Steve Hardison, imagining what he would teach me if he commuted with me. I was Ritt, the Small, and he was Rimi, the Giant.

It took me eleven years to get that book published. For years, it collected dust on a bookshelf. The manuscript was complete, but the story wasn't over. It took another crisis for me to wake up my inner Giant.

In 2019, my wife and I got divorced, and that put me into another tailspin. I needed something to hold me in this world. I was ready to leave, and I saw no point in all of the chaos I felt I was going through. My book helped anchor me and gave me a purpose on which to focus. I dove in! In 2020, the book was published—a beautifully illustrated work with hints of some of the finest talents in the world. People like Steve Hardison, Richard Paul Evans, Jenna Evans Welch, Steve Chandler, Stephen McGhee (there are many Steve's in the coaching industry), Debbie Roth, and many others influenced this work.

This book was a children's book written for adults that is changing the world; a book that is becoming a Pixar animated movie. A book that reaches the hands of 100 million people worldwide. A book influences people from every background, culture, race, socio-economic status, age, and ability to strive for their highest potential. A book that creates a world

The Giants and the Smalls: The Adventure of Rimi and Ritt is a book that teaches coaching from the perspective of The Ultimate Giant, Steve Hardison.

It's amazing how one conversation, a single dialogue, can influence a global movement. I am eternally grateful that Steve let me stand on his shoulder that fateful day. He helped me catch a vision that never faded and is now making a difference in every reader.

I AM a Giant! I AM a Giant because of people like Steve Hardison.

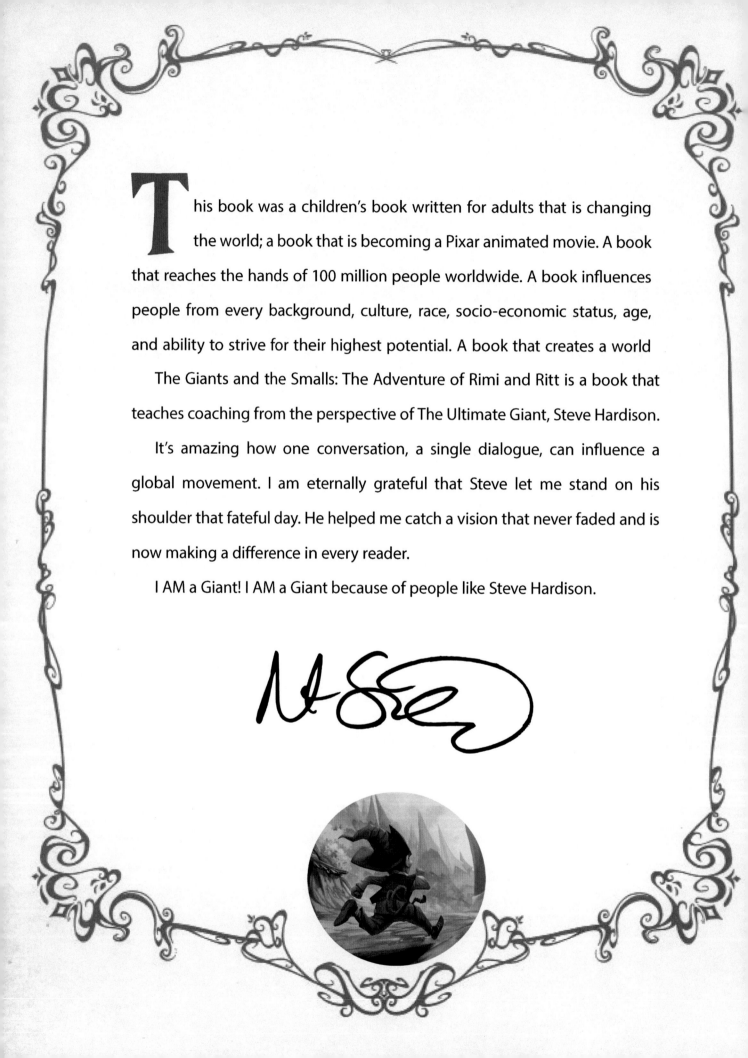

DISCUSSION POINTS

Discussion points for parents, guardians, teachers, and avid readers:

- What was your favorite part of the story?
- Have you ever felt like a Small? Have you ever felt like a Giant? When?
- How would you react if you were Ritt at the beginning of the story when other Smalls told him he couldn't become a Giant?
- What questions would you ask if you could meet a Giant?
- Why did Ritt grow? What would you think if you started growing like Ritt?
- Was there anything in the book that surprised you?
- If you could be a character in the book for one day, who would you chose to be? Why?
- If you could have dinner with Rimi, the Giant, what would you ask him?
- Have you ever learned something new that was hard at first, but got easier the more you practiced?
- What kind of Giant things would you like to create in your life?
- When was a time you felt scared like Ritt? How did you show courage?
- If you had to pick one color to describe the book, what color would you pick? Why?
- If you had to describe this book in one word, what word would you choose?
- Were you satisfied with the ending of the story? Why?
- Were there any new words that you learned from reading the book?
- What do you think the author wanted us to take away from this book?
- If you could ask the author one question, what would you ask?
- Do you have a friend who you think would like this book? Who is it? Why?
- If the author were to write a sequel to this book, what do you think would happen to the characters?
- How can you be a Giant after reading this book?

Come join *The Tribe of Giants* today at:
https://www.facebook.com/groups/tribeofgiants/

This is a private group for owners of the book *The Giants and the Smalls.*

AUTHOR | *My name is Nicholas Townsend Smith (Nick), and I'm a Performance Coach and founder of Clearpath Training (clearpathtraining.com). I work with individuals, entrepreneurs, and organizations to develop tools, systems, and processes to reach their goals, increase performance, and improve personal and organizational efficiency. I know that whether you are striving to reach personal or organizational goals, it takes effort in the right things long enough to win. I've coached and worked with leaders in organizations, sales professionals, individuals from around the world, and experts in fields ranging from professional arm wrestlers to New York Times best-selling authors. My ability to help individuals see the gaps in their performance and create a clear path to change is powerful and unique.*

I hold a Master's degree in Industrial/Organizational Psychology, am a devoted father, and am the author of The Art of Accomplishment *(Available on Audible),* Sowing Seeds, How I Went From Zero To Number One In Sales in Only Five Months, *and* Green Goo. *My other works include* No String Selling *and* The Boy and the Bird.

ILLUSTRATOR | *My name is JuanManuel Tumburús. I was born in Buenos Aires, in 1981. I began my career in animation studios (HookUp, Framing), until I established myself as an illustrator.*

I worked on digital painting and backgrounds for two feature films (El Arca, a family-oriented Spanish-language tale that offers a lyrical, comic, and surprisingly gentle animated take on the Biblical story of Noah's Ark).

I have been a freelance illustrator since 2007, have illustrated more than 1,000 comic pages for the USA (Boom studios, Kickstart), and have participated in countless advertising spots.

Additionally, I was published in Heavy Metal Magazine, Dark Horse Presents, Pictus, Fierro Magazine, OVNI Press, among others. I am currently engaged in teaching, preproduction animation, video games, and comic books.

THE GIANT'S PATH

How does a Giant
Create big things that we see?
Can you do that?
And how could it be?

Well, you have big dreams
And hopes deep within
That will change your whole world
If you'll only begin

To see that vision
As clear as the now
And work toward it daily
Though you don't quite know how

The pathway you choose
Is up to you
There are millions of them
Anyone will do

And if it ends up
One doesn't pan out
Then just pick another
And try not to pout

Because your pathway
Is not like another
Nope, Not like your cousin
Your friend or your mother

It is your own
and that's the fun
Just know where you're going
And run run run

Get there by chicken
Or a billy goat
Get there by digging
Or by car or by boat

You'll zig, and you'll zag
There's not just one way
Keep trying new paths
Til you get there one day

Your dream is your own
Its no-ones to share
Be a dancer, inventor
Or one who does hair

Be the best you can be
Every step of the way
For you can be anything
And that starts today

Trust in yourself
That every step that you take
Will lead to your dream
And that's no mistake

For when you step forward
Yep, Into your vision
You'll change your whole life
With that simple decision

And don't ever quit
On the dreams that you make
Cause you can do anything
If you'll stay awake

Now this much I promise
That it's up to you
That you can anything
You decide to do

So go out, imagine
Anything that you can
Go after it daily
Over your entire life span

For you are a giant
Its always in there
You can be anything
If you will take care

Just make up the dream
The path will appear
As you step forward, trusting
Your dreams will get clear

And giants keep growing
They reach goals and then...
They do it all over
Again and again.

I love you. I love you,
Can you love you too
Who are you, my friend?
A Giant, that's who!

Based on the book, The Giants
and the Smalls: The Adventure of
Rimi and Ritt.
Giantsandsmalls.com

If you could see you the way I do,
you'd humble at the sight.
You'd never have another fear
of if you'd be alright.

You'd step into your greatness
and help the world to see
that life becomes amazing
when you Be who you're meant to be.

Yet out of prudence and smallness
we choose to please the world,
and instead of the success that we deserve
we find our plans unfurled.

That's so not fair to who you are
and what God made you for
'cause you were made to change the world.
Yes, that's what's at your core!

So, don't play Small in this incredible world
where you can be anything you dream.
You're a Giant, and that's what's needed
despite how things might seem.

Step into your greatness and let it grow!
The world's waiting for your light.
It's needed more than you'll ever know,
so go after it with your might!

See your power; lean into it.
I can't wait to see you lift!
This is your purpose; your life's true path,
to inspire others with your gift!

Nicholas Townsend Smith
The Giants and the Smalls

THE GIANT'S CREED

From ancestral writings of long ago,
the first Giants of all time
made promises to live at their highest potential
and pursue the upward climb.

While Smalls and Giants are born the same,
their choices change their way,
and those that choose the higher path
will live as Giants one day.

The road's not easy, the path takes work,
you'll start over day by day.
You'll have to watch your behaviors and thoughts,
and every word that you say.

To make this promise do not step back
for you can return to Small.
Your vigilance is a vital step,
being a Giant means giving your all.

So here's your promise for this Giant path.
Don't take lightly the words that ensue.
A Giant's committed in all that it does,
for what you commit to is what you do.

A Giant is serving, and loving, and kind,
and will stretch for challenging things.
A Giant is trusting, hardworking, and honest,
and enjoys the fruit that this brings.

Giant's explore possibilities
and never leave things to chance.
Which means a Giant always strives for growth,
while finding time to laugh and dance.

A Giant's not entitled
to the creations other Giants create.
Instead, a Giant will lend a hand
in behalf of another teammate.

A Giant understands there's more to learn,
and studies as much as they can.
A Giant's courageous in every step
and remembers from where they began.

A Giant has the utmost integrity
regardless of what unfolds.
A Giant respects every creature on Earth,
and the potential that each one holds.

A Giant dreams impossible dreams
and finds beauty all around.
And finally, A Giant believes there's plenty
for all and that all things can abound.

So If you'll make this commitment now,
that's no Small task you see.
You'll grow in a world of possibility,
and we promise, a Giant you'll be.

-Nicholas Townsend Smith

LEARN MORE
POINT YOUR PHONE HERE

Made in the USA
Las Vegas, NV
23 November 2021